The Missing

Part 1

Story Street 🎈
Cakes School
Summer Fair
Gates Open
2 O'Clock
Games 🐤
Bring Your
Friends
Bouncy Castle Today

story by Kaye Umansky
illustrated by Roger Horgan

There was a summer fair at
Story Street School.

Sam went with her mum.
She wore her best dress and
her new shoes.

"We must hurry," said Mum.
"I am doing the face painting."

The gates opened at two o'clock.

Inside there were lots of fun
things to see and do.

There were books, toys and
clothes for sale.

There were cakes, plants and
pots of jam for sale.

There were games to play.

Best of all, there was a Bouncy
Castle!

Sam's mum got out her face paints.

"Here is some money, Sam,"
she said. "Go and have fun."
"Thanks Mum," said Sam.

She ran to the Bouncy Castle.

Ben, Jojo and Mouse were there.

"Hurry up Sam!" they shouted.

"Take off your shoes please,"
said Mr Lee.

Sam took off her shoes in a hurry.

"Here I come!" she shouted.

Soon she was jumping up and down.
It was fun.

"Time up," said Mr Lee.

They all got off the Bouncy Castle and
began to put on their shoes.

Sam looked for her shoes.

Oh no! They had gone!

Now what?